Kids

By Liza Charlesworth

ISBN: 978-1-339-02681-7

Art Director: Tannaz Fassihi; Designer: Tanya Chernyak
Photos ©: p2: fizkes/Shutterstock.com. All other photos @ Getty Images.

3 4 5 6 7 8 9 10 68 32 31 30 29 28 27 26 25 24

Printed in Jiaxing, China. First printing, August 2023.

MSCHOLASTIC

Can a kid fix a truck? Yes!
This kid and his dad fixed it up.

Can a kid jump in a pond? Yes!
This kid jumped in and swam.

Can a kid ask for help? Yes!
This kid's mom helped him a lot.

Can a kid sniff a sock? Yes!
This kid just sniffed it. Yuck!

Can a kid dress up? Yes!
This kid dressed up as a snack.

Can a kid get rest? Yes!
This kid rested with a pet.

Can a kid huff and puff? Yes!
This kid huffed and puffed
and did win.